Exclusive Distributors:
Music Sales Limited
8/9 Frith Street,
London W1V 5TZ, England.
Music Sales Pty Limited
120 Rothschild Avenue,
Rosebery, NSW 2018,
Australia.

Order No.NO90609
ISBN 0-7119-5015-6
This book © Copyright 1995 by Wise Publications

Music Sales' complete catalogue describes thousands of titles and is available
in full colour sections by subject, direct from Music Sales Limited.
Please state your areas of interest and send a cheque/postal order for £1.50 for postage to:
Music Sales Limited, Newmarket Road, Bury St. Edmunds, Suffolk IP33 3YB.

Wise Publications
London/New York/Paris/Sydney/Copenhagen/Madrid

Love Me Do

Words and Music by John Lennon and Paul McCartney

*Harmonica arr. for gtr.

1-4. Love, love me do, ___ you know I love you. ___ I'll

al - ways be true, ___ so ___ please

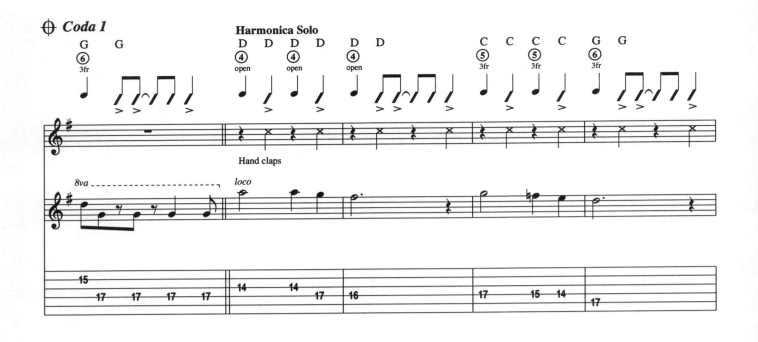

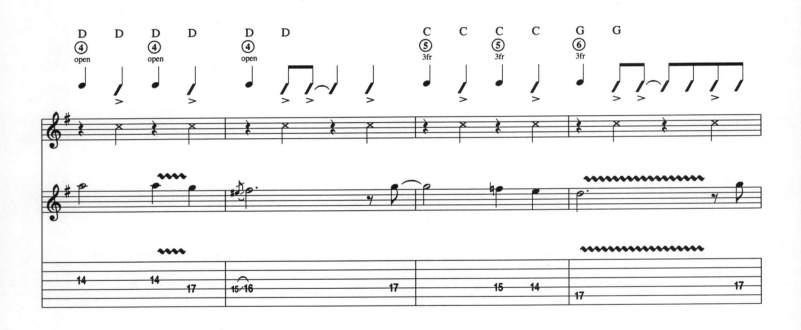

Please Please Me

Words and Music by John Lennon and Paul McCartney

From Me To You

Words and Music by John Lennon and Paul McCartney

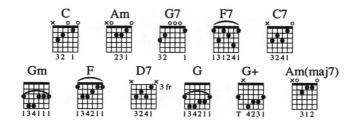

Intro

Moderately Fast ♩ = 138

Gtrs. 1 & 2 (acous. & elec.)

Da da da da da dum dum da.   Da da da da da dum dum

* Gtr. 3

* Harmonica arr. for gtr.

Verse

Gtr. 3 tacet

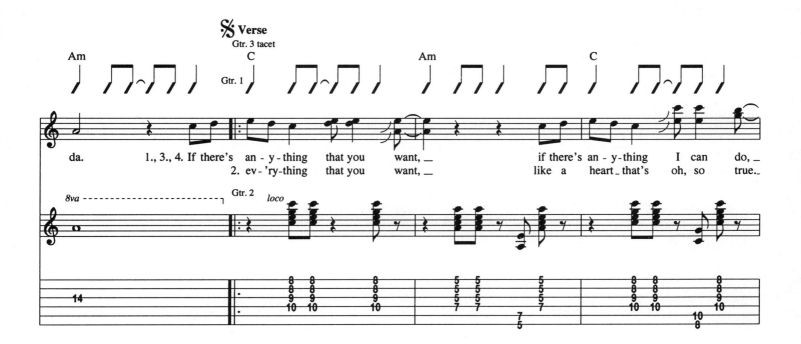

da.   1., 3., 4. If there's an-y-thing that you want, —   if there's an-y-thing I can do, —
      2. ev-'ry-thing that you want, —   like a heart _ that's oh, so true.—

just call on me ___ and I'll send it a - long ___ with love,_

To Coda 1

To Coda 2

1.

from me ___ to ___ you. ___

2.

2. I got ___

I got

(cont. in slash)

Bridge

Gtrs.
1 & 2

arms that long to hold _ you and keep you by my ___ side. I got

Gtr. 2 (cont. in notation)

Gtr. 2

She Loves You

Words and Music by John Lennon and Paul McCartney

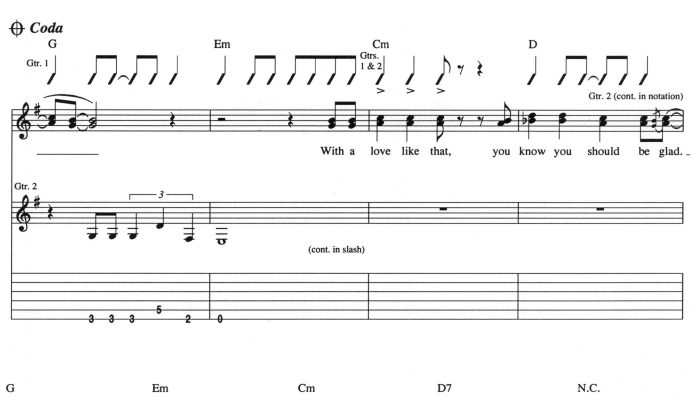

With a love like that, you know you should be glad.

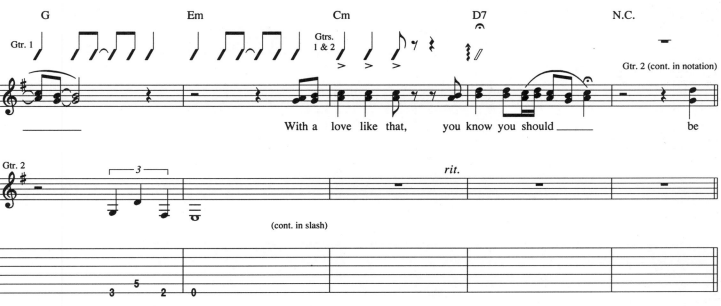

With a love like that, you know you should _____ be

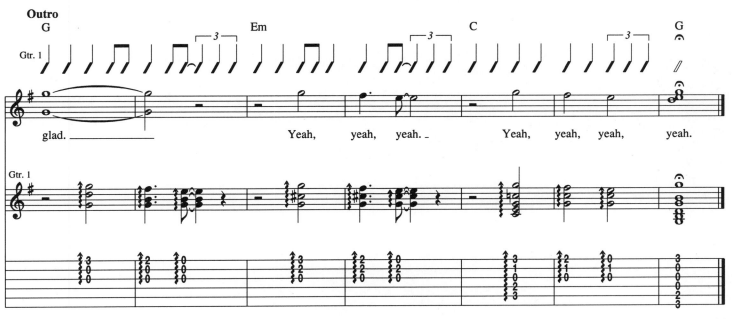

glad. _____ Yeah, yeah, yeah. _____ Yeah, yeah, yeah, yeah.

I Want To Hold Your Hand

Words and Music by John Lennon and Paul McCartney

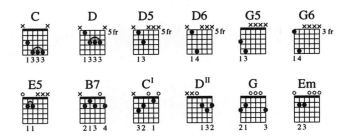

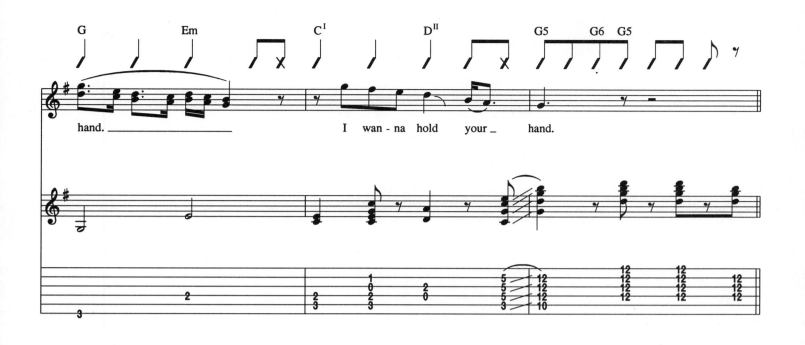

hand. _____ I wan - na hold your _ hand.

Bridge
Gtr. 2 tacet

Upper part tacet 1st time

And when I touch you I feel hap - py in - side. ___

let ring – – – – – ⌐   let ring simile

It's such a feel - ing that my love,   I can't hide, __   I can't hide,__

All My Loving

Words and Music by John Lennon and Paul McCartney

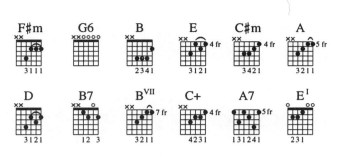

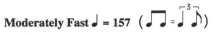

Moderately Fast ♩ = 157

1., 3. Close your eyes ____ and I'll kiss ____ you, to-
2. ____ that I'm kiss-ing the

* Voc. harm. on 3rd verse only.

mor - row I'll miss ____ you. Re - mem - ber ____ I'll
lips I am miss - ing, and hope that ____ my

3. Close your eyes

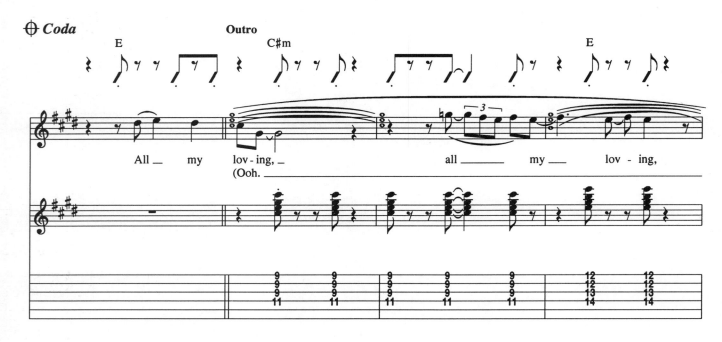

All — my lov-ing, — all ——— my — lov - ing,
(Ooh. ——————

ooh, — all — my — lov-ing, I will send — to — you.
—) (Ooh. —————————)

Can't Buy Me Love

Words and Music by John Lennon and Paul McCartney

A Hard Day's Night

Words and Music by John Lennon and Paul McCartney

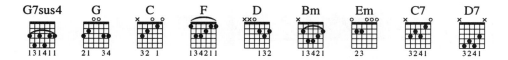

And I Love Her

Words and Music by John Lennon and Paul McCartney

could nev - er die, _____ as _____ long as I _____

have you near _ me. _____

D. S. al Coda

⊕ Coda
Guitar Solo

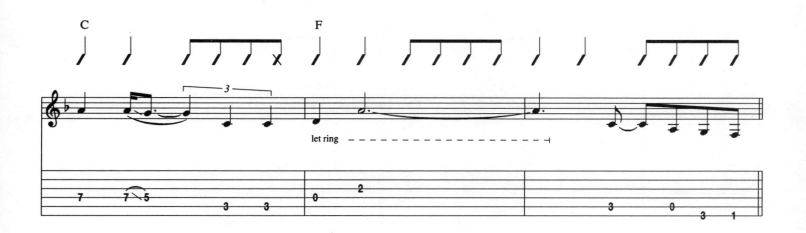

Verse

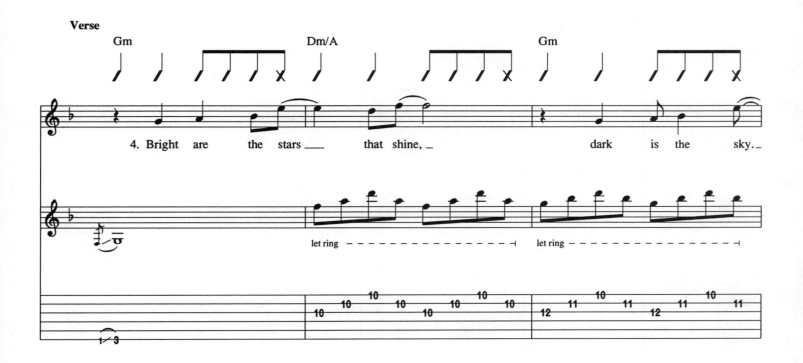

4. Bright are the stars ___ that shine, ___ dark is the sky. ___

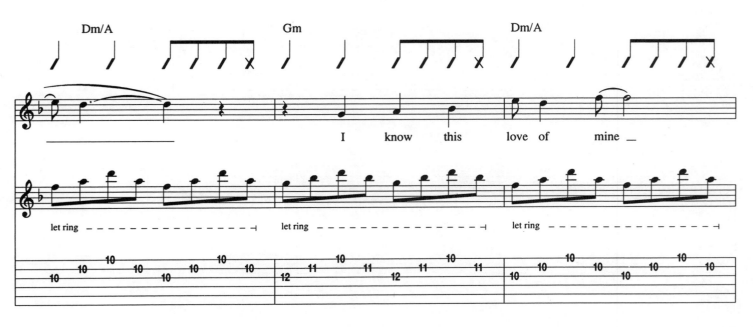

I know this love of mine ___

will nev-er die. ____ And I love ____ her. _____

Eight Days A Week

Words and Music by John Lennon and Paul McCartney

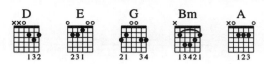

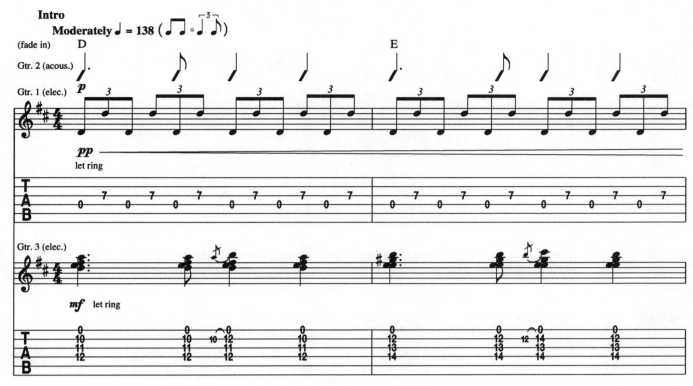

*Slight P.M. next 8 meas.

Gtr. 3 tacet

Gtr. 2

love, babe, ___ guess you know it's true. ___
___ girl, ___ al - ways on my mind. ___

Gtr. 1

Hope you need my love, babe, ___ just like I need you. ___
One thing I can say, ___ girl, ___ love you all the time. ___

3rd time only

Oh. _____

Chorus

Hold me, ___ love me. ___ Hold me, ___ love me. ___ I

Sing harmonies 2nd and 4th times only.

36

To Coda 2 ⊕

ain't got noth-in' but love, {1., 3., 4. babe, / 2. girl, —} eight days a week. __

Bridge

Eight days a week, I love _____ you.

D.S. al Coda 1
(no repeat)

To Coda 1 ⊕

Eight days a week is not e-nough to show I care. __

I Feel Fine

Words and Music by John Lennon and Paul McCartney

*fdbk. occurs as a vibrating string striking a nearby fingernail.

Chorus

I'm in love with her __ and I __ feel __ fine.

End Rhy. Fig. 1

Bridge

I'm so glad that she's my lit-tle girl. __
(Oo, oo.)

She's so glad, she's tell-in' all __ the world __ 3.,5. that her ba-
(Oo, oo.)

Verse

Gtr. 1: w/ Rhy. Fig. 1, simile

__ by buys her things, __ you know, __ he buys her dia-mond rings, __ you know, __ she said __

Ticket To Ride

Words and Music by John Lennon and Paul McCartney

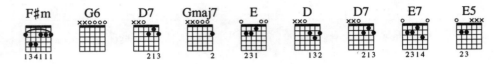

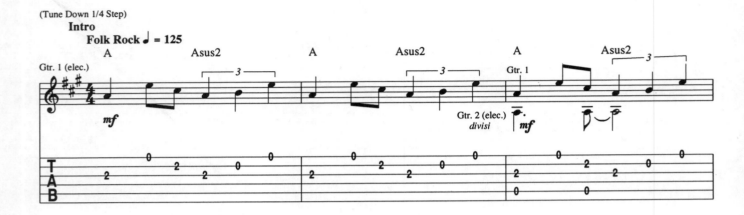

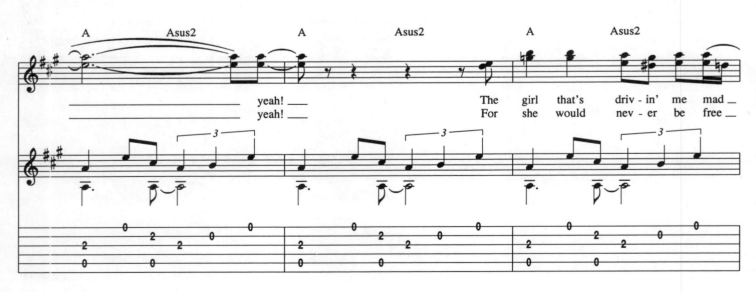

is go-in' a-way.
when I was a-round.

End Rhy. Fig. 1

*Gtr. 1 tabbed to the left

Chorus

Gtr. 2 tacet

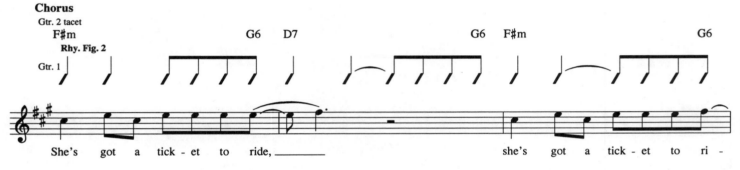

She's got a tick-et to ride, _____ she's got a tick-et to ri -

- hi - hide, _ she's got a tick-et to ride, _ and she don't care. _

(cont. in notation)

End Rhy. Fig. 2

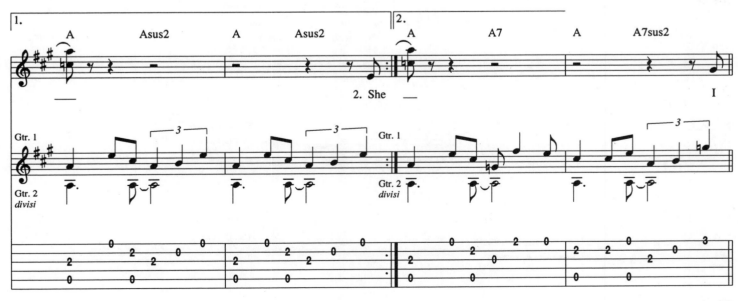

2. She _

I

Yesterday

Words and Music by John Lennon and Paul McCartney

Tune Down 1 Step:
①=D ④=C
②=A ⑤=G
③=F ⑥=D

Intro
Moderately ♩ = 98

G5

Verse

1. Yes - ter - day, __

Gtr. 1 (acous.)

mf let ring throughout

F#m B7 Em Cmaj7 D7

all my trou - bles seemed so far a - way. __ Now it looks as though __ they're

G5 G/F# Em7 A C5 G5

here to stay. __ Oh, I be - lieve __ in yes - ter - day. __

Help!

Words and Music by John Lennon and Paul McCartney

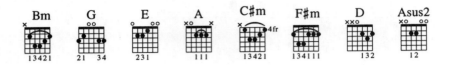

Additional Lyrics

2. And now my life has changed in oh, so many ways.
   My independence seems to vanish in the haze.
   But every now and then I feel so insecure.
   I know that I just need you like I've never done before.

You've Got To Hide Your Love Away

Words and Music by John Lennon and Paul McCartney

We Can Work It Out

Words and Music by John Lennon and Paul McCartney

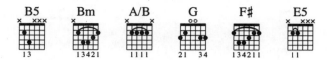

Bridge

* Play 1st time only

** Play 2nd time only

that it's a crime, _____

so I will __ ask you once a - gain.   gain.

D.S. al Coda

⊕ *Coda*
Chorus

We can   work__ it out. __   We can   work__ it out. ___

Day Tripper

Words and Music by John Lennon and Paul McCartney

Got a good rea - son
She's a big tea - ser.
Tried to please her,

for tak-ing the eas - y way out, ___ now.
She took me half ___ the way there, ___ now.
she on - ly played ___ one night stands, ___ now.

She was a

Chorus

Gtr. 3: w/ Fill 1, 1st time
Gtr. 3: w/ Fill 2, 2nd time
Gtr. 3: w/ Fill 4, 3rd time (see p. 64)

Gtr. 3: w/ Fill 3, 2nd time

Day _____ Trip - per;

one way tick - et, yeah. ___
one way tick - et, yeah. ___
Sun-day driv - er, yeah. ___

It took me

60

Interlude

Gtr. 3: w/ Riff A

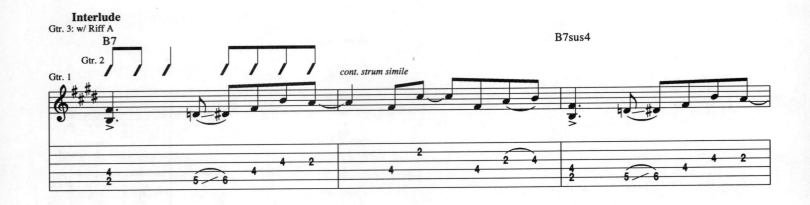

Guitar Solo

Riff A
Gtr. 3

Gtr. 4: w/ Rhy. Fill 2

Breakdown

N.C. (E7)

Gtr. 2: w/ Rhy. Fig. 1

E   E7   E

E7   E   E7

D.S. al Coda
(take 1st ending)

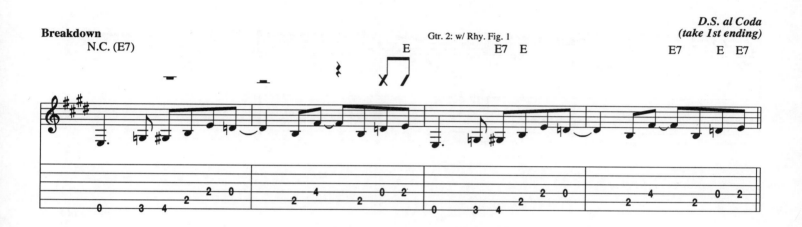

⊕*Coda*

Breakdown

Gtrs. 1 & 2

N.C. (E7)

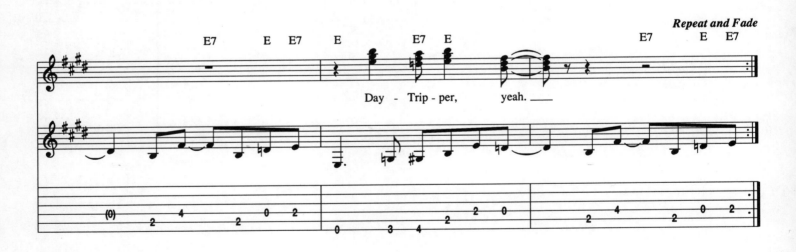

Drive My Car

Words and Music by John Lennon and Paul McCartney

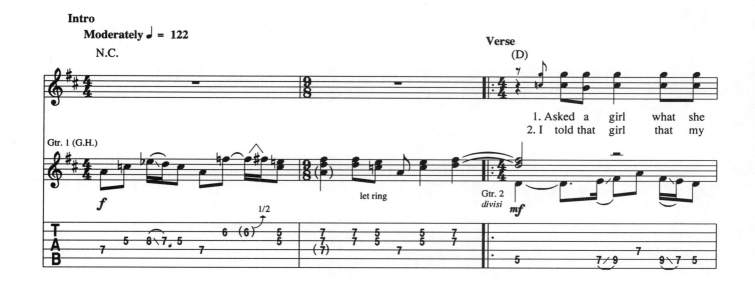

Guitar Solo

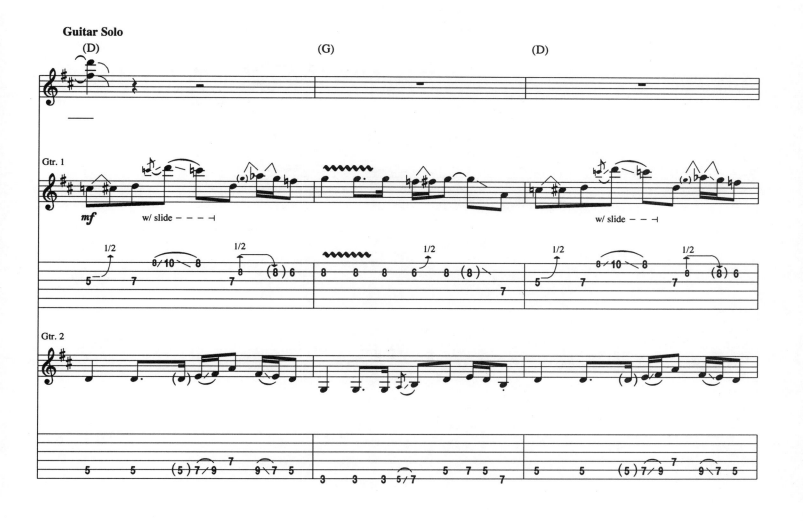

Norwegian Wood
(This Bird Has Flown)

Words and Music by John Lennon and Paul McCartney

All Gtrs.: Capo II

Intro

Moderately ♩. = 60

* Gtr. 1 (acous.)

(J.L.)

let ring throughout

* Notes tabbed at 2nd fret played as open strings.

† Gtr. 2 (acous.)

† Gtr. 3 (acous.)
divisi

*Gtr. 4 (12 str. acous.)

† Sitar arr. for Gtrs. 2 & 3
* Notes tabbed at 2nd fret played as open strings.

Verse

1. I once had a girl,___ or should I say she once had me. She showed me her

So I looked a-round and I no-ticed there was-n't a chair.

2. I sat on a rug bid-ing my time, drink-ing her

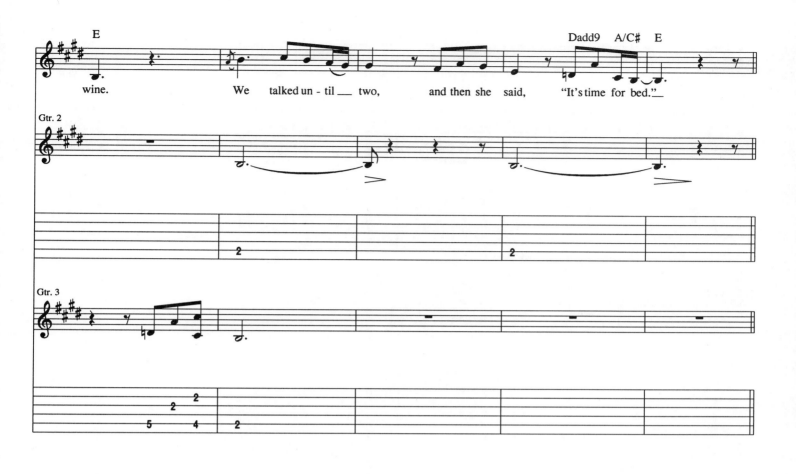

wine.   We talked un - til __ two,   and then she said,   "It's time for bed." __

Interlude

75

Dadd9 Aadd6/C# E

She

Bridge
Gtrs. 2 & 3 tacet
Gtrs. 1 & 4: w/ Rhy. Figs. 2 & 2A

Em   A

told me she worked in the morn - ing and start - ed to laugh. ___   I

Em   F#m7   B

told her I did - n't and crawled off to sleep in the bath. ___

Verse
Gtrs. 1 & 4: w/ Rhy. Figs. 1 & 1A

E   Dadd9   A/C#

3. And   when I a - woke   I was a - lone, ___   this bird had

Gtr. 2

flown.   So   I   lit   a   fire,   is-n't   it   good,   Nor-we-gian   Wood.

Nowhere Man

Words and Music by John Lennon and Paul McCartney

Gtr. 1: Capo II

Verse

Moderately ♩ = 122

A Cappella

1. He's a real no - where __ man, sit - ting in __ his

no - where __ land, mak - ing all __ his no - where plans for no - bod - y.

*Gtr. 1 (acous.), (J.L.)

mf let ring throughout

*Notes tabbed at 2nd fret played as open strings.

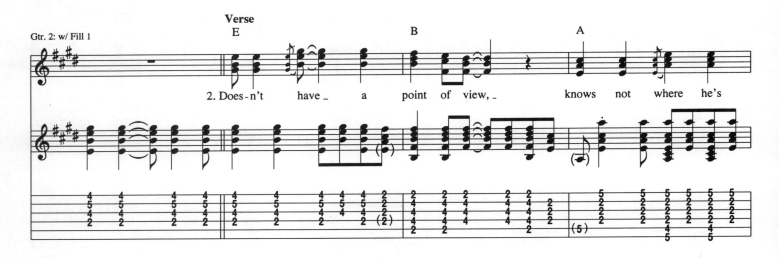

Gtr. 2: w/ Fill 1

Verse

2. Does - n't have __ a point of view, __ knows not where he's

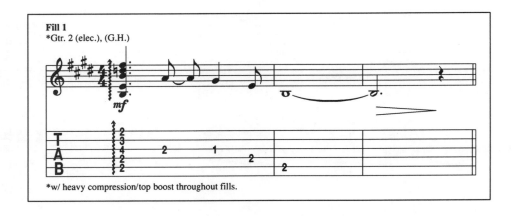

Fill 1
*Gtr. 2 (elec.), (G.H.)

mf

*w/ heavy compression/top boost throughout fills.

go-ing to.___ Is-n't he ___ a bit ___ like you ___ and me?_____

%% **Chorus**

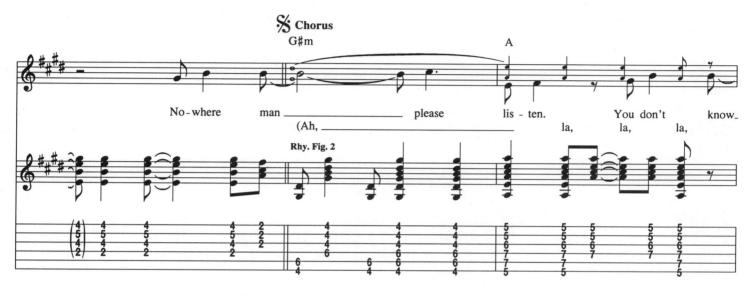

No-where man _____ please lis-ten. You don't know___
(Ah, _____ la, la, la,

___ ah, _____ what ___ you're miss-ing. No-where ___ man, ___ the
la, la, la, ah, _____

Fill 2
Gtr. 2

world _____ is at your com-mand. _____

la, la, la, ah, _____ la, la, la, la,

Guitar Solo

la.)

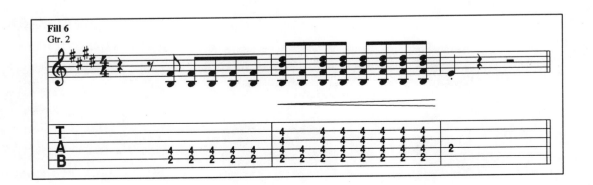

G#m   F#m7   Gtr. 2: w/ Fill 4   B

'til some-bod-y else lends you a hand.

ah, la la la, ah, la la la la.)

Verse

Gtr. 1: w/ Rhy. Fig. 1

E   B   A   E

4. Does-n't have a point of view, knows not where he's go-ing to.

Gtr. 2: w/ Fill 5   ***D.S. al Coda***

F#m   Am   E

Is-n't he a bit like you and me? No-where man

⊕ *Coda*

Verse

Gtr. 1: w/ Rhy. Fig. 1

E   B   A

5. He's a real no - where man, sit-ting in his

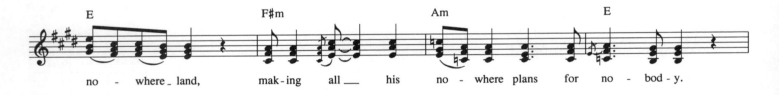

E   F#m   Am   E

no - where land, mak-ing all his no - where plans for no-bod-y.

Fill 4
Gtr. 2

Fill 5
Gtr. 2

Tag
Gtr. 1: w/ Rhy. Fig. 1, last 4 meas.

83

Michelle

Words and Music by John Lennon and Paul McCartney

Gtr. 1: Capo V

Intro
Moderately ♩ = 118

*Notes tabbed at 5th fret played as open strings.

Chorus
Gtr. 2 tacet

Mi - chelle, ma belle, these are words that
(Ooh, ooh.

go to-geth-er well, my Mi-chelle.)

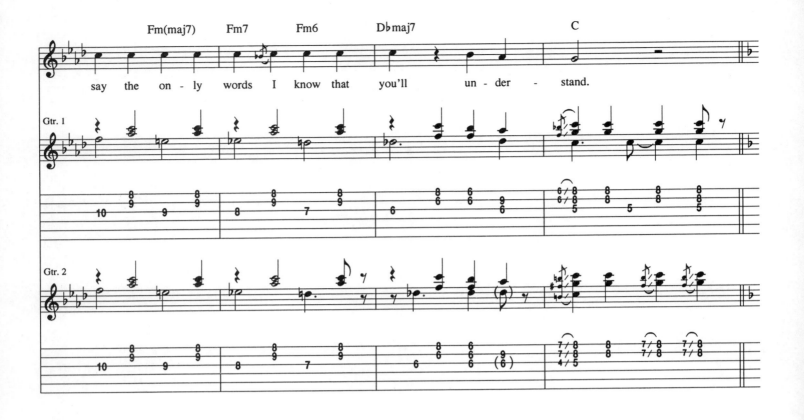

say the on-ly words I know that you'll un-der - stand.

Chorus

Mi - chelle, ma belle, sont des mots qui
(Ooh, ____ ooh. ____

vont tres bien en - semble, ___ tres bien en - semble.

2. I

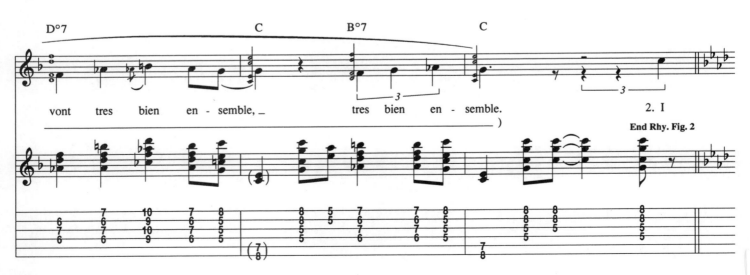

Guitar Solo

Gtr. 2 tacet

I love you. ooh.

(Ooh,

*Gtr. 3 (elec.)

steady gliss.

Gtr. 1

* Neck pick up w/treble rolled off.

3. I

Verse

Gtr. 1: w/ Rhy. Fig. 1

Gtr. 3 tacet

want you, I want you, I want you, I think you know by

(Ooh,

Gtr. 3

now, I'll get to you some - how. Un -

ooh.)

In My Life

Words and Music by John Lennon and Paul McCartney

Piano Solo

Girl

Words and Music by John Lennon and Paul McCartney

Chorus

girl, _____ fffff, _____ girl, _____ girl. _____

(breathe in)

2. When I

End Rhy. Fig 2

Rhy. Fig. 2

Verse

Gtr. 1: w/ Rhy. Fig. 1, simile

think of all the times _ I tried so hard to leave her, she will turn to me and start to cry. And she

prom-is-es _ the earth _ to me and I ____ be-lieve _ her, af-ter all this time I don't know why. Ah, _

Chorus

Gtr. 1: w/ Rhy. Fig. 2, simile

girl, _____ fffff, _____ girl, _____ girl. _____

(breathe in)

Bridge

She's the kind of girl who puts you down when friends are there, you feel a

(Tit, tit, tit, tit, tit, tit, tit, tit, tit, tit, tit, tit, tit, tit, tit, tit,

98

man must break his back to earn his day of lei- sure? Will she still be - lieve. it when he's dead? Ah, —

Chorus
Gtr. 2 tacet

girl, _____ fffff, _____ girl, _____ girl.
(breathe in)

Interlude

Gtr 2

Gtr. 1

Out-Chorus

Gtrs. 2 & 3 tacet
Begin Fade

Fade Out

girl, _____

fffff, _____
(breathe in)

girl, _____ girl. _____

Gtr.1

Paperback Writer

Words and Music by John Lennon and Paul McCartney

Eleanor Rigby

Words and Music by John Lennon and Paul McCartney

Verse

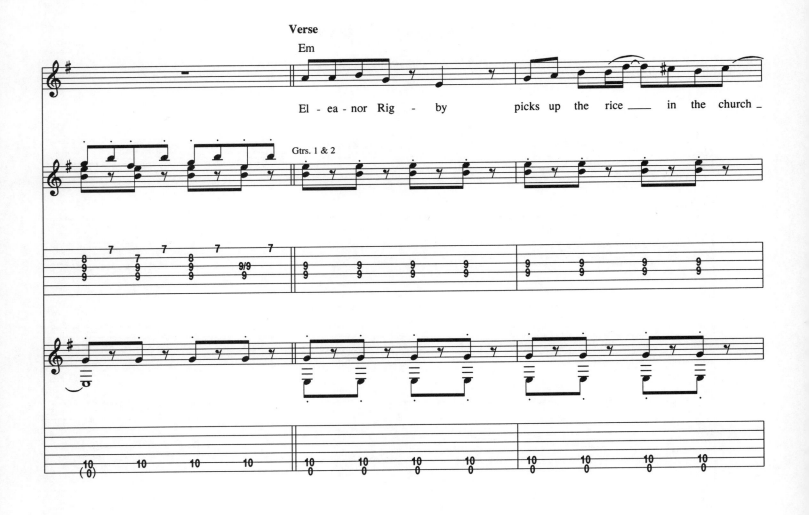

El - ea - nor Rig - by   picks up the rice ___ in the church ___

___ where a wed - ding has been, ___   lives in a dream. ___

Waits at the win-dow, wear-ing a face __ that she keeps __ in a jar __ by the door, __

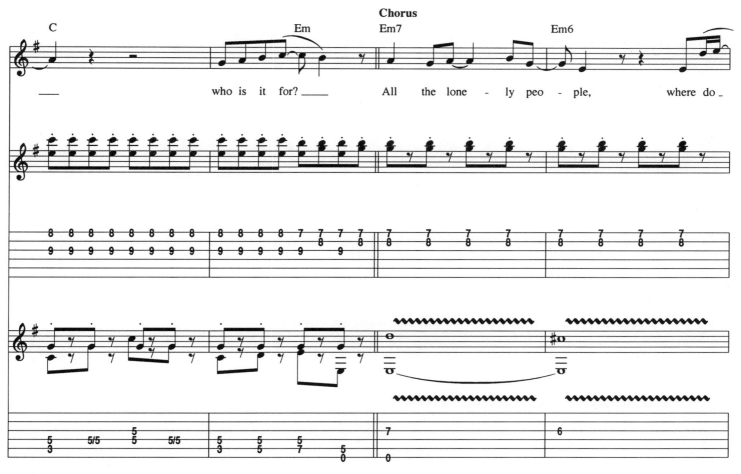

Chorus

__ who is it for? __ All the lone-ly peo-ple, where do __

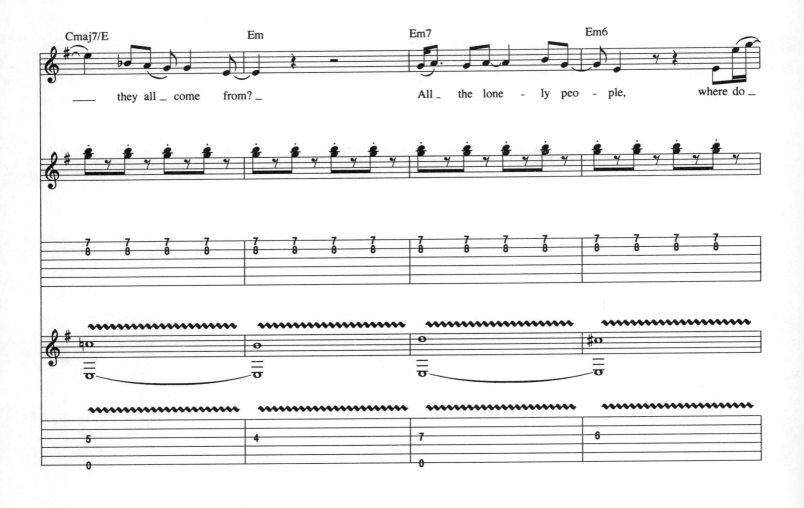

they all _ come   from? _   All _ the lone - ly peo - ple,   where do _

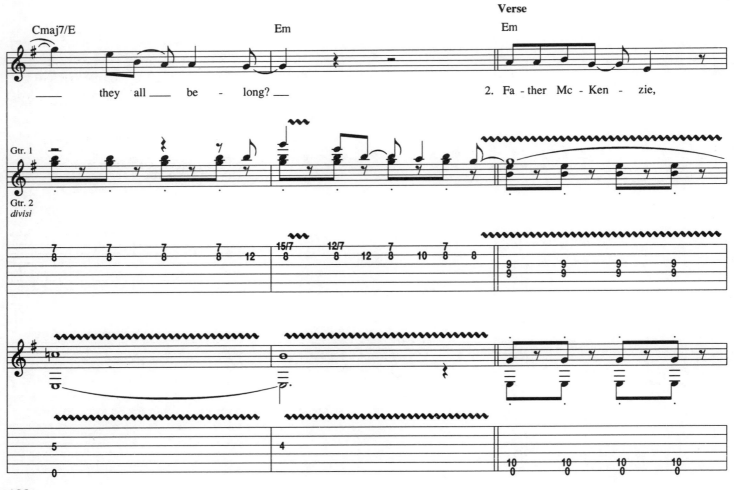

they all ___ be - long? ___   2. Fa - ther Mc - Ken - zie,

writ-ing the words of a ser-mon that no one will hear, no

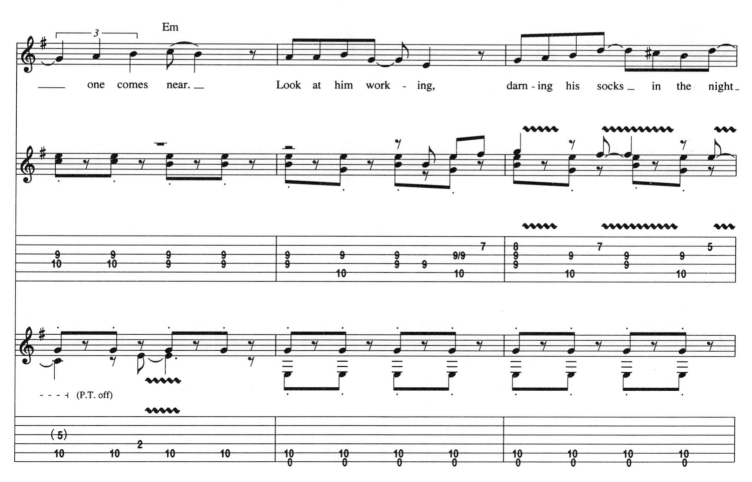

one comes near. Look at him work-ing, darn-ing his socks in the night

_____ when there's no - bod - y's there. _____ What does he care? _____

Chorus

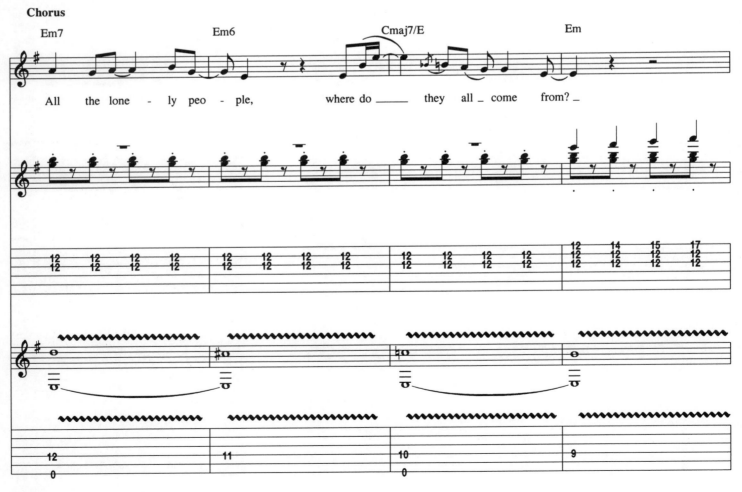

All   the lone - ly peo - ple,   where do _____ they all _ come from? _

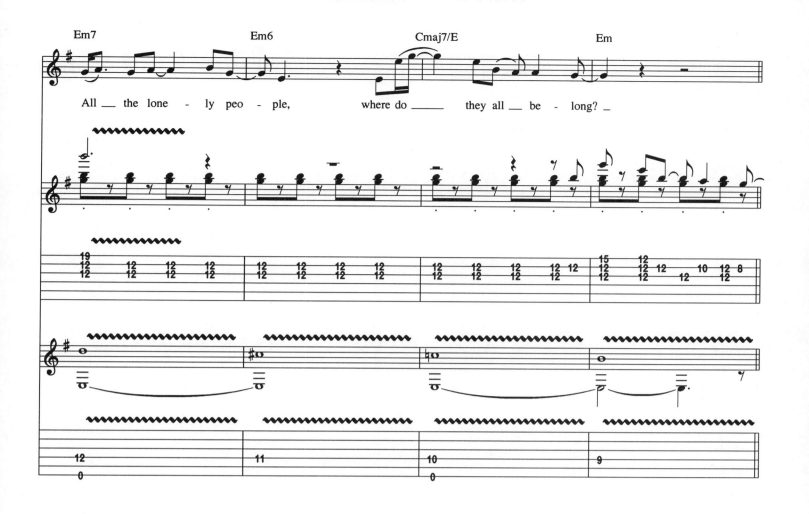

All — the lone - ly peo - ple, where do _____ they all — be - long? —

Chorus

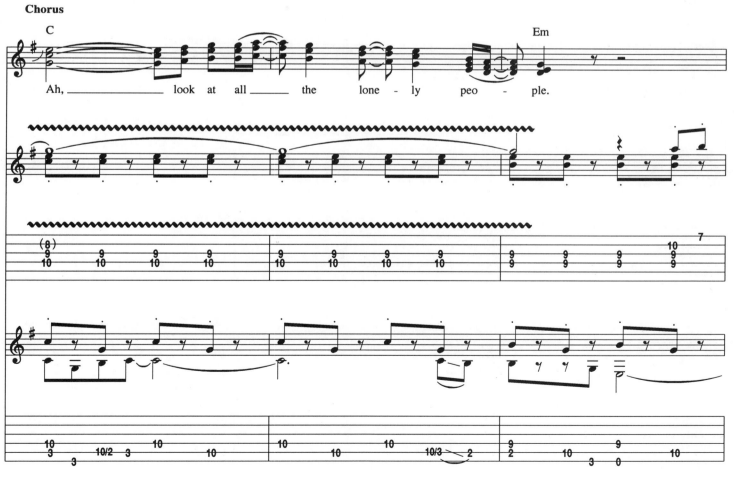

Ah, _____ look at all _____ the lone - ly peo - ple.

111

Ah, _____ look at all ___ the lone - ly peo -

P.T. on - (P.T. off)

- ple.

Verse

3. El - ea - nor Rig - by

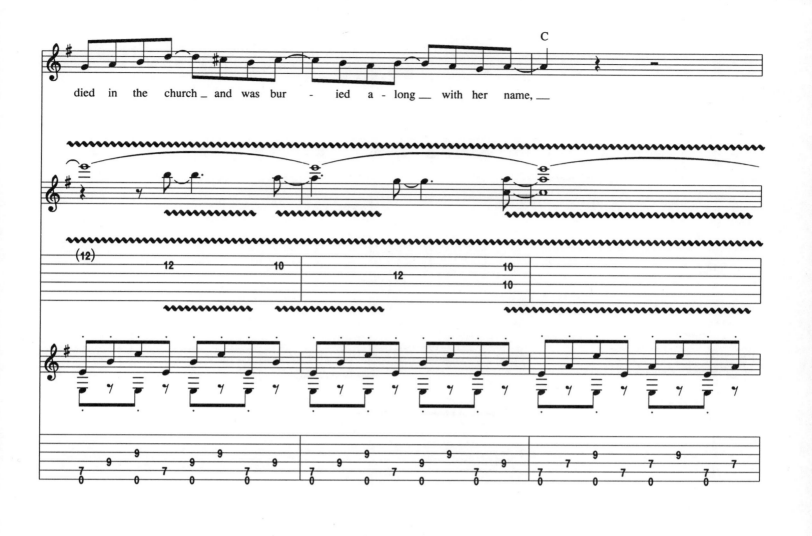

died in the church _ and was bur - ied a - long _ with her name, _

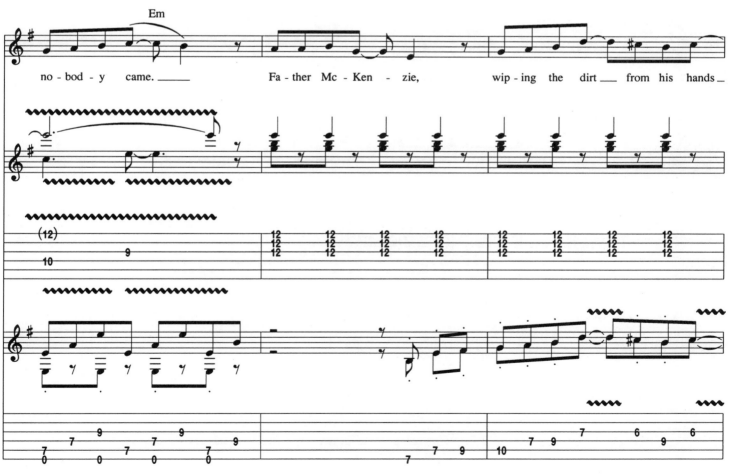

no - bod - y came. _____ Fa - ther Mc - Ken - zie, wip - ing the dirt _ from his hands _

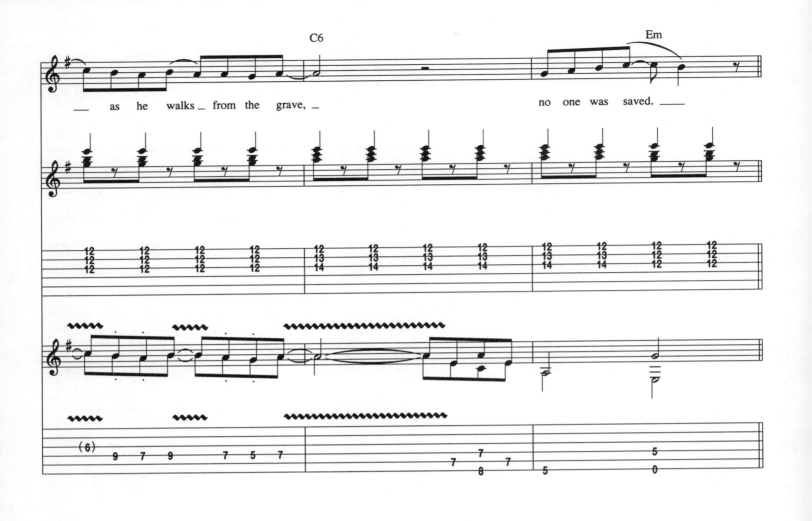

as he walks ___ from the grave, ___ no one was saved. ___

Chorus

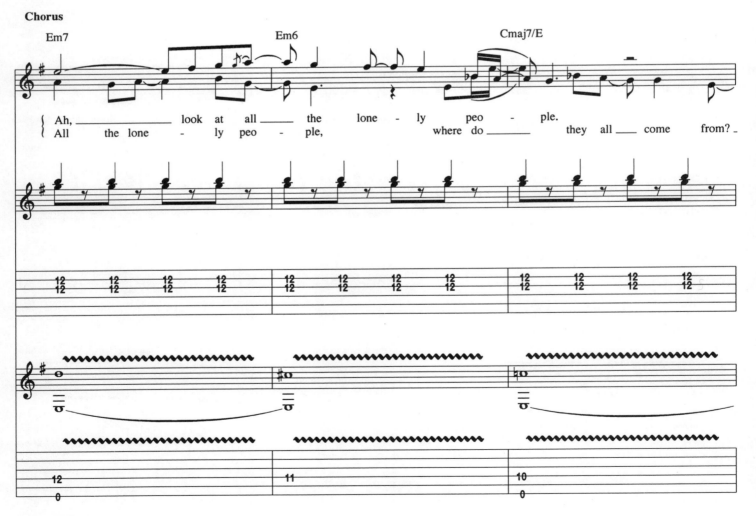

Ah, ___ look at all ___ the lone - ly peo - ple.
All the lone - ly peo - ple, where do ___ they all ___ come from? ___

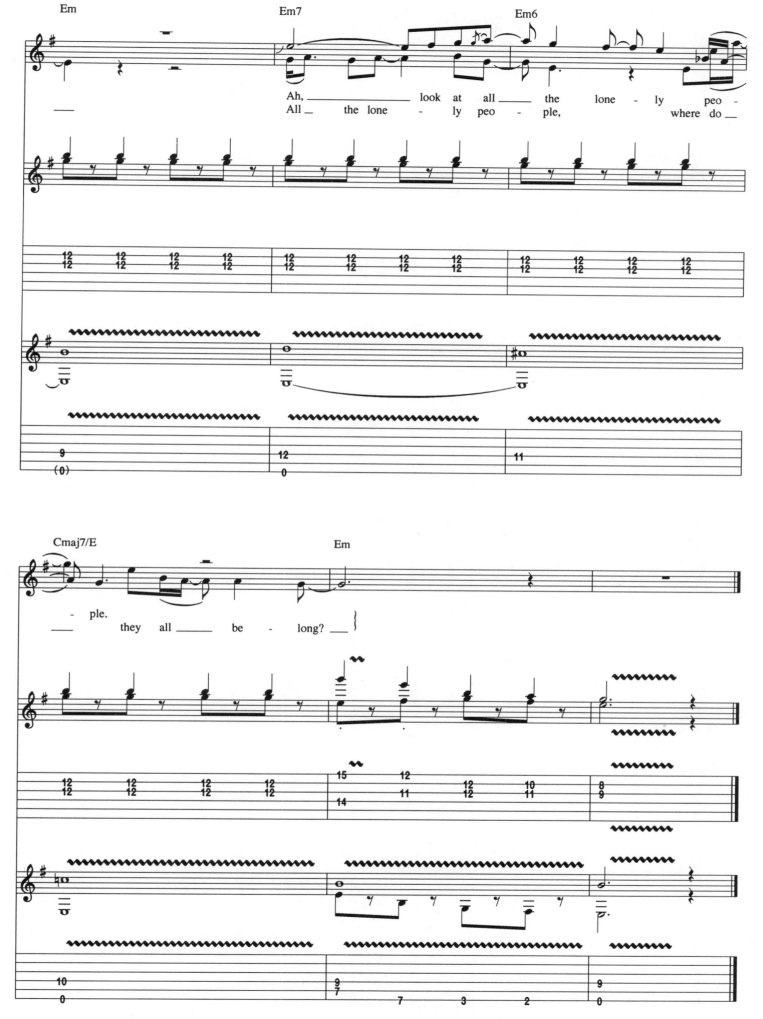

Yellow Submarine

Words and Music by John Lennon and Paul McCartney

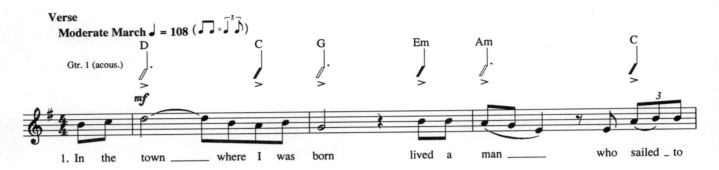

Tune Down 1/2 Step:

① = Eb ④ = Db

② = Bb ⑤ = Ab

③ = Gb ⑥ = Eb

Verse
Moderate March ♩ = 108

Gtr. 1 (acous.)

1. In the town ____ where I was born lived a man ____ who sailed _ to

sea. And he told _____ us of his life ____ in the land _____ of sub - ma -

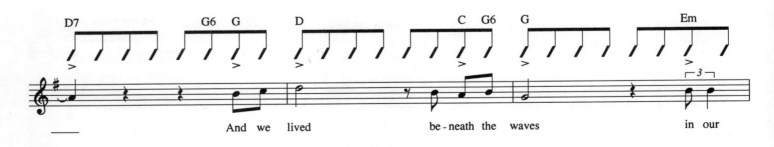

rines. So we sailed _____ on to the sun 'til we found _____ the sea of green. _

And we lived be - neath the waves in our

Chorus

We all live in a

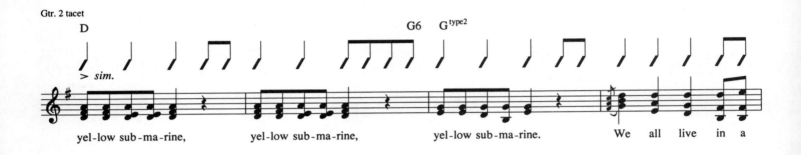

Gtr. 2 tacet

yel-low sub-ma-rine,   yel-low sub-ma-rine,   yel-low sub-ma-rine.   We all live in a

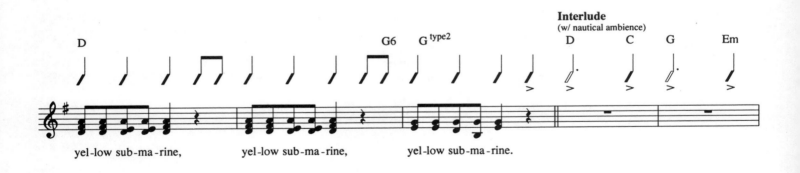

Interlude
(w/ nautical ambience)

yel-low sub-ma-rine,   yel-low sub-ma-rine,   yel-low sub-ma-rine.

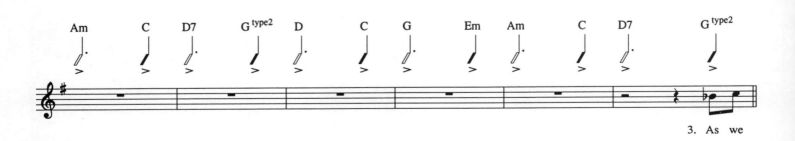

3. As we

119

NOTATION LEGEND

Printed and bound in Great Britain by Halstan & Co. Ltd., Amersham, Bucks.
3/97 (27277)